STAR WARS

JABBA THE HUTT

STAR WARS

JABBA THE HUTT

BOXTREE

Jim Woodring
Script

Art Wetherell
Pencils

Monty Sheldon
Inks

Steve Dutro
Lettering

James Sinclair
Colours

Steve Bissette
Cover Pencils

Cam Kennedy
Cover Inks

Scott Tice
Logo & Book Design

Ryder Windham
Editor

First published in Great Britain in 1995 by Boxtree Limited,
Broadwall House, 21 Broadwall, London SE1 9PL

10 9 8 7 6 5 4 3 2 1

ISBN: 0 7522 0704 0

Printed and bound in Great Britain by Cambus Litho, East Kilbride. A CIP catalogue
entry for this book is available from the British Library.

THAT WORD "FRIENDLY" AMUSES ME.

I HAVE NO FRIENDS, THANKS BE. WHO CAN AFFORD A FRIEND? WHO CAN AFFORD TO TRUST A FRIEND?

A FRIEND IS A WEAK SPOT, A ROTTEN SPOT-- A LIABILITY.

I CAN SAY THE SAME.

BUT I DO MAKE ONE EXCEPTION. ONLY ONE EXCEPTION. YOU.

I CAN SAY THE SAME.

THAT IS WHY I AM CELEBRATING YOUR VISIT WITH THIS JUBJUB. IT'S RARE THAT WE HAVE A JUBJUB THESE DAYS.

IT IS AN ANCIENT TRADITION, AND SELDOM OBSERVED ANY-MORE, I'M SORRY TO SAY.

I APPRECIATE THE HONOR.

YES, BUT I CAN SEE THAT YOU'RE EAGER TO GET TO BUSINESS, AND SO AM I. COME TO THE TABLE.

LET'S BEGIN. FIRST, I WANT TO TELL YOU THAT I CONSIDER YOUR THREAT TO PLACE A BOMB IN MY PALACE TO BE CHEAP, UNDIGNIFIED, AND BENEATH YOU.

I WAS NOT JOKING. I DID INTEND TO PUT A BOMB IN HERE.

I TOOK YOU AT YOUR WORD. DO YOU KNOW KOSH KURP?

ONLY THROUGH REPUTATION. IT IS AN HONOR, SIR.

HRNT.

YOU KNOW THEN THAT KURP IS THE EMPIRE'S TOP CONSULTING SPECIALIST, AND THE GREATEST LIVING AUTHORITY ON OFFENSIVE DEVICES.

OF COURSE.

HA! O GAAR, YOU KNOW I LIVE TO SERVE YOU! KNOWING HOW YOU FEEL ABOUT DR. PONTAK...

I TOOK THE LIBERTY OF BRINGING HIM ALONG.

IT IS! IT IS! DR. PONTAK!

IN THE FLESH.

HOW DID YOU ... NO, DON'T TELL ME! BUT THIS IS TOO GOOD TO BE TRUE!

NO, IT'S DEFINITELY STERILE. THINK BACK; YOU DIDN'T SPECIFY A FERTILE MALE!

THINK YOU'RE CLEVER!

NO HARD FEELINGS? WE ALL HAVE TO BE BESTED SOME TIME.

TRUE ENOUGH.

I WONDER IF I COULD INTEREST YOU IN AN ACCESSORY FOR DR. PONTAK.

PROBABLY NOT. WHAT IS IT?

HOW ABOUT HIS BRAIN?

WHAT?!

NOW YOU MAY HAVE YOUR MEN LOAD THE SPICE, O GAAR, AND I'LL BE ON MY WAY.

WAIT. I'D LIKE KOSH KURP TO HAVE A CLOSER LOOK AT THAT GRENADE. I'LL NOT BE BLUFFED.

CERTAINLY, YOUR SUSPICIONS ARE UNDER-STANDABLE.

NO...NO... IT WAS TOO QUICK.

YOU WILL BE COMPENSATED.

YOU KEEP OUT OF THIS! IT HAS NOTHING TO DO WITH YOU!

IT HAS EVERYTHING TO DO WITH ME.

I KNEW ABOUT YOUR QUEST TO FIND SONOPO BOMOOR. I KNEW THAT GAAR WAS SONOPO BOMOOR.

I KNEW THAT A BOMB THREAT WOULD CAUSE THE EMPIRE TO SEND YOU HERE.

YOU WERE THE BOMB. AND YOU PLAYED YOUR PART TO PERFECTION.

FORMER MINIONS OF THE LATE GAAR! BEHOLD YOUR NEW MASTER, KOSH KURP! SERVE HIM AS YOU DID THE GAAR...

...AND MAY PROSPERITY REIGN.

THE END

Jabba the Hutt
The Hunger of Princess Nampi

In his cunning and treacherous meeting
with the notorious Gaar Suppoon, Jabba
the Hutt proved his status as the most vile
gangster in the galaxy. The meeting ended
in the Gaar's death, and Jabba greatly
expanded his own wealth and power.

Jabba and his minions have left the Gaar's
planet, and are flying their treasure-laden ship
by the smugglers' route to Tatooine. But it's a
long journey to the sand planet, and there are
some things that not even Jabba can anticipate!

YOU'RE BACK! THAT MEANS I LOSE A HUNDRED CREDITS TO BIB.

YOU BET HIM I WOULDN'T RETURN? THAT WAS FOOLISH, SCUPPA.

WELL, I THOUGHT *HE* WOULDN'T RETURN EITHER.

WE'VE TAKEN ON TEN KORGS. ADJUST THE THRUST MODULATOR ACCORDINGLY.

TEN KORGS? FROM THAT SLUMP-FACED TIGHTWUMP? JABBA, YOU ARE TRULY THE KING OF NEGOTIATORS.

AND YOU ARE THE EMBODIMENT OF FLATTERY HIMSELF, SCUPPA -- AS EVER.

MUST KEEP IN PRACTICE, TEN KORGS! AH, JABBA-- IT'S LIKE OLD TIMES!

YES, EXCEPT THAT INSTEAD OF BEING COMRADES, I AM NOW YOUR *MASTER*. DON'T FORGET THAT.

I WOULDN'T HAVE IT ANY OTHER WAY. YOU WERE ALWAYS MY BETTER, JABBA, EVEN WHEN WE WERE FIGHTING SIDE BY SIDE. IT IS AN HONOR TO BE YOUR SERVANT.

THAT'S THE PROPER WAY TO FEEL, SCUPPA.

THIS IS N2090 CALLING UNIDENTIFIED FREIGHTER. COME IN PLEASE!

WE READ YOU, N2090. WHAT ARE YOU?

WE ARE A NUFFIN TRADE TEAM WHO HAVE COMANDEERED A PIRATE CRAFT.

COMANDEERED? YOU MUST EXPLAIN, N2090. BE ADVISED WE HAVE OUR PULSE ROCKETS TRAINED ON YOU.

OUR TRADE TEAM WAS WAYLAID BY PRIVATEERS IN THE AMPUROON MINING DISTRICT OF WASKIRO. BY CHANCE WE WERE ARMED WITH LBK'S AND WERE ABLE TO ESCAPE IN THIS SHIP.

YOU HAD LBK'S, HM? I WASN'T SURE THEY WERE BEYOND PROTOTYPE.

THESE WERE THE PROTOTYPES. THEY AREN'T PERFECT BUT THEY GOT US OUT OF THERE.

TAKE THE HUTT TO THE LARDER!

TELL HER NOTHING, SCUPPA! DIE IF YOU MUST, BUT PRESERVE OUR HONOR!

TENDERIZE HIM, BUT TAKE CARE NOT TO BREAK HIS JAW. HE'LL NEED IT TO BEG FOR MERCY.

YOU CAN SHARE HIS FATE, YOU CREATURE, OR YOU CAN BE INTELLIGENT AND TELL ME HOW TO GET PAST THE VOICE-CODE.

THE TRUTH IS I DO NOT KNOW, YOUR MAJESTY. JABBA SHARES HIS DEEPEST SECRETS WITH NO ONE.

TAKE THIS ONE TO THE LARDER ALSO!

WELL, I MAY BE ABLE TO TALK SOME SENSE INTO HIM.

IF YOU FAIL, I WILL TAKE CONSOLATION BY CHEWING YOUR FLAYED HIDES.

I SUGGEST YOU LET HIM SIMMER DOWN A BIT, AND THEN I'LL SEE IF I CAN'T MAKE HIM LISTEN TO REASON.

HE TRUSTS ME.

YOU SEEM SINGULARLY REASONABLE FOR A FREEBOOTER. I UNDERSTAND THAT YOU ARE HIS SECOND IN COMMAND, HM?

THEN AS HE IS MY CAPTIVE AND YOU ARE MY GUEST, HIS AUTHORITY REVERTS TO YOU, NO?

YES.

TECHNICALLY, YES. YES, IT DOES.

THEN USE YOUR AUTHORITY TO PERSUADE JABBA TO RELINQUISH HIS TROVE. DO THIS AND I WILL SPARE YOUR LIFE.

VERY WELL, YOUR HIGHNESS.

HE MAY PUT UP A BIT OF A FUSS, BUT I'M CERTAIN I CAN MAKE HIM SEE REASON.

YOU SCOB-CHOBBLING, DOUBLE-HUSKING, COB-KEELED SON OF A SAND LOUSE! YOU'VE THROWN IN WITH HER, HAVE YOU?

TRAITOR! FLAP-EATER! SCROGGINATING PURSWILLION!

IF I GET MY HANDS ON YOU, I'LL OPEN YOU UP LIKE A NINNY! YELLOW-GUTTED GUMP-MULLET!

I KNEW YOU'D BE UPSET, OLD FRIEND...

...BUT THERE'S NO HELP FOR IT. IF YOU DON'T HAND OVER YOUR TROVE, SHE'LL SIMPLY KILL US BOTH AND PERHAPS FIND A WAY TO GET IT LATER.

THEN SO BE IT! I'LL NEVER GIVE UP MY HORDE TO THAT FEMALE GUT-HEAP!

JABBA... YOU REALIZE THAT SINCE YOU ARE INCARCERATED AND I AM NOT, I AM IN CHARGE OF THE SHIP.

WHAT?

AND AS CAPTAIN, I AM ORDERING YOU TO TELL ME HOW TO BYPASS THE VOICE-CODE.

ROT IN BOBOQUEEQUEE, YOU SCRUNTY, PRUGNUFICATING SPOGGICK!

BACK, YOU!

FROM WHAT I HEARD, YOUR POWERS OF PERSUASION ARE NOT WHAT YOU CLAIMED. I AM OUT OF PATIENCE.

YOUR HIGHNESS, I HAVE INDEED FAILED.

I AM A WARRIOR, SO PLEASE LET ME DIE WITH HONOR BY MY OWN HAND.

PLEASE GIVE ME A SWORD, THAT I MAY BURY IT IN MY UNWORTHY ENTRAILS.

OH, THIS ONE HAS SPUNK!

GUARDS, CLEAR THE CHAMBER! LET ME BE ALONE WITH THIS DOOMED SOLDIER!

YOU HAVE... QUALITIES. I FEEL ATTRACTED TO YOU.

OF COURSE, NO MALE COULD BE IMMUNE TO YOUR CHARMS--

I SHOULD DESPISE YOU... BUT I FEEL A POWERFUL SYMPATHY BETWEEN US.

I FEEL IT TOO.

HOW CAN THIS BE? IT IS *MADNESS!*

YOUR *HIGHNESS,* THE HEART HAS ITS OWN REASONS--

BUT WHAT AM I SAYING? I AM A *COMMONER,* AND I HAVE FAILED YOU.

IF ONLY... BUT NO. IT CAN *NEVER* BE.

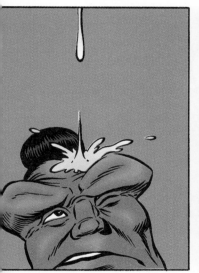

WHAT'S THE MATTER, PRINCESS?

DON'T YOU THINK I *KNOW* THAT YOU FIND ME REPULSIVE?

I HEARD THAT REMARK YOU MADE ABOUT MY SCENT.

HUH? NO. THAT WAS THE *OTHER GUYS.* I HAPPEN TO THINK THAT YOU SMELL *CLASSY.*

YOU'RE *VERY STRONG,* AND I *ADMIRE* THAT IN A FEMALE. MY MOTHER WAS WAS A STRONG BEING. I, UH...

HOW DO I KNOW YOU AREN'T JUST FLATTERING ME TO SAVE YOUR HIDE, OR WORSE, TO SAVE THAT EXECRABLE HUTT?

JUST LOOK INTO MY EYES.

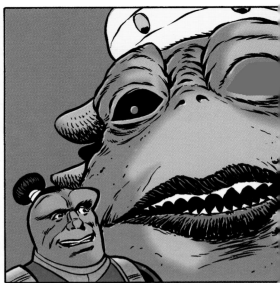

GUARDS! BRING THIS CHAMPION ROYAL GARMENTS! HE WILL BE MY PRINCE!

DARLING! IT WAS MEANT TO BE!

DRESS THE GROOM WHILE I PREPARE MYSELF!

I'LL COUNT THE MOMENTS!

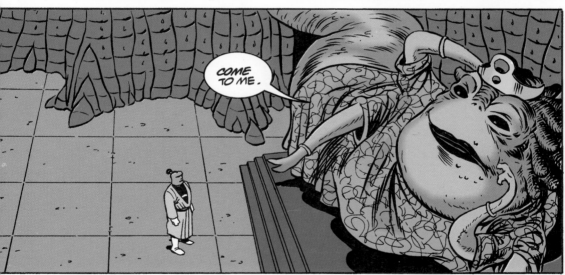

I BELIEVE I MADE A BAD CHOICE. NO AMOUNT OF TREASURE CAN BE WORTH THIS DREADFUL FEELING OF UNFULFILLMENT.

TO EACH THEIR OWN, YOUR HIGHNESS.

WHERE ARE MY GUARDS?

DEAD, YOUR HIGHNESS. VICTIMS OF MY CUNNING, AS YOU WILL BE UNLESS YOU DO EXACTLY AS I SAY.

I DON'T SEE THAT YOU ARE ARMED.

BUT I AM. SCUPPA WAS A GOOD COMRADE, BUT HE HAD HIS PRICE.

I KNEW THAT IF HE WERE SUFFICIENTLY TEMPTED TO BETRAY ME, HE WOULD DO SO.

I HAD TO HAVE THE MEANS OF KILLING HIM AT WILL. THE OPPORTUNITY AROSE SOME TIME BACK WHEN SCUPPA RECEIVED A HEAD WOUND IN BATTLE.

IT WASN'T SERIOUS, BUT IT REQUIRED SOME PATCHING. I HAD THE SURGEON WHO FIXED HIM UP IMPLANT A SMALL VIAL OF CONCENTRATED XENOBORIC ACID IN HIS SKULL.

THE VIAL HAS VALVES THAT CAN BE OPENED BY REMOTE CONTROL. THAT VIAL IS NOW IN YOUR BELLY, YOUR HIGHNESS...

...AND HERE IS THE CONTROL.

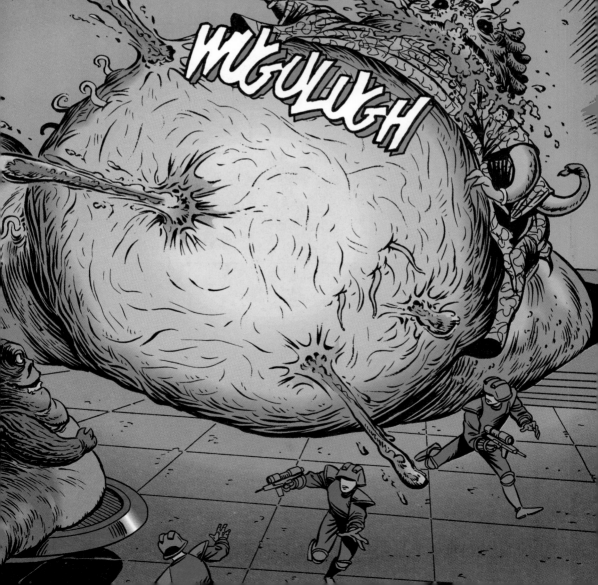

WUGULUGH

THE END

Jabba the Hutt
The Dynasty Trap

Following his meeting with Gaar
Suppoon, Jabba the Hutt and his men
attempted to overtake a Nuffin freighter,
only to find themselves in the massive
clutches of Princess Nampi of Orooturoo.
Through the loss of Jabba's second in
command, Jabba defeated Nampi, and once
again increased his power.

Although it may prove difficult to sell the
captured Nuffin freighter on the black market,
Jabba is only encouraged by the possibility of
even greater fortune.

YOUR EXCELLENCY. IF I MIGHT MAKE A SUGGESTION....

YES. CONTRIBUTE SOMETHING MEANINGFUL TO MY LIFE, BIB.

I ONLY WANTED TO SUGGEST, YOUR EXCELLENCY, THAT THE SHIP ITSELF HAS VALUE, AND CABROOL NUUM'S BASE IS NOT FAR AWAY-- HE WOULD BUY IT FOR HIS OPERATION, I AM SURE.

HA! GOOD THINKING, BIB!

HUH ... CABROOL NUUM DEALS IN SLAVES ALSO. I COULD SELL HIM THIS LOT....

AH, BUT I FEEL TOO GOOD RIGHT NOW TO DO THAT!

TAKE 'EM TO THE PORTAGE BAY AND SET 'EM LOOSE IN SPACE!

DON'T LEAVE THE SHIP. RESPOND TO MY COMMAND ONLY.

YES, YOUR EXCELLENCY.

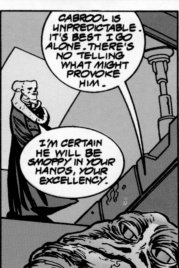

CABROOL IS UNPREDICTABLE. IT'S BEST I GO ALONE. THERE'S NO TELLING WHAT MIGHT PROVOKE HIM.

I'M CERTAIN HE WILL BE SMOPPY IN YOUR HANDS, YOUR EXCELLENCY.

HLMF. WE'LL SEE...

AH, JABBA THE HUTT, DEAR BROTHER! I AM DELIGHTED TO SEE YOU!

CABROOL NUUM, I AM YOUR SERVANT. IT IS AN HONOR TO BE RECEIVED IN YOUR QUARTERS.

OH, YOU CAN STOP ALL THAT STUFF. LEAVE IT TO THE OTHERS.

SO, I HEAR OF YOUR EXPLOITS EVERYWHERE NOWADAYS!

I AM AMBITIOUS ONLY FOR THE HONOR OF THE FIELD, SHA CABROOL.

EXCELLENT! I UNDERSTAND YOU HAVE A CRAFT FOR ME.

YES, A NUFFIN FREIGHTER.

STRIPPED?

NO, INTACT. EMPTY, OF COURSE.

I'LL INSTRUCT MY PAYMASTER TO GIVE YOU DOUBLE THE MARKET RATE.

I ONLY WANT WHAT'S FAIR, SHA CABROOL.

I SAID I'D GIVE YOU DOUBLE. DON'T REFUSE MY GENEROSITY, JABBA.

DAD, RUSK SAYS YOU TOLD HIM HE COULD LEAD THE DAWN PATROL.

DON'T INTERRUPT, CHILD. AH, JABBA, MY DAUGHTER NORBA.

CHARMED TO MAKE YOUR ACQUAINTANCE.

HOW D'YA DO? DAD, IS THAT TRUE? DID YOU SAY HE COULD?

I CAN'T ACHIEVE ANYTHING AROUND HERE WITHOUT HER DELIBERATELY TRYING TO MESS THINGS UP FOR ME!

WHERE ARE YOUR MANNERS, SON?

JABBA, MY BOY RUSK.

PLEASED TO MAKE YOUR ACQUAINTANCE.

JABBA IS AN OLD AND RE-SPEC-TED FRIEND AND COL-LEAGUE...

OH, EXCUSE ME. HOW DO YOU DO?

...AND I DON'T WANT HIM TO HAVE TO HEAR YOU TWO QUARRELING.

WHO AM I TALKING TO?

ME AND RUSK, DAD. YOUR CHILDREN.

heh...WELL, I GUESS I KIND OF WENT OFF THE DEEP END. FORGET ALL THAT, KIDS. I WAS JUST BLOWING OFF STEAM. JUST RUN ALONG, AND DON'T LET ME HEAR ANY MORE SQUABBLING.

C'MON, RUSK.

ANY CHILDREN OF YOUR OWN, JABBA?

NO.

KIDS! I LOVE 'EM, BUT THEY DRIVE YOU CRAZY.

URNT...

I WAS SORRY TO HEAR ABOUT THE DEATH OF YOUR WIFE, SHA CABROOL.

YES, VERY SAD.

SHA CABROOL, WHAT DO YOU HEAR FROM VH CHUSKER?

WHY ARE YOU ASKING ME ABOUT HIM?

WELL, YOU ARE STILL CLOSE ASSOCIATES, AREN'T YOU?

YESSS... VU CHUSKER HAS BECOME THE MOST DANGEROUS BEING IN MY LIFE. BUT YOU KNOW THAT, OF COURSE.

NO, I KNOW ALMOST NOTHING OF VU CHUSKER. WE'VE NEVER MET.

OH, COME NOW, JABBA-- I'M SURE YOU KNOW HIM. I'M SURE YOU KNOW HIM VERY WELL! THE WAY YOU SAID HIS NAME... TELLS ALL!

YOU HAVE MY WORD, SHA CABROOL -- I'VE NEVER MET VU CHUSKER.

THEN I SUPPOSE YOU'D HAVE NO OBJECTION TO KILLING HIM... EH?

NO... NO SPECIAL OBJECTION. BUT WHY WOULD I KILL HIM?

BECAUSE I'M OFFERING YOU THE CHANCE TO RENDER ME SERVICE BY KILLING VU CHUSKER.

I'M SORRY, SHA CABROOL, BUT I MUST RESPECTFULLY DECLINE.

YOU'RE NOT IN A POSITION TO DECLINE. YOU'LL KILL VU CHUSKER OR I'LL KILL YOU. REALLY, I'D JUST AS SOON, YOU DUPLICITOUS SACK OF FILTH.

SHA CABROOL, PLEASE GET A GRIP ON YOURSELF. I AM NOT YOUR HENCHMAN.

YOU'VE GOT TONIGHT TO THINK IT OVER. TOMORROW YOU'LL AGREE TO DEMONSTRATE YOUR ALLEGIANCE TO ME BY EXTERMINATING VU CHUSKER OR YOU'LL BE THE SADDEST HOUSEGUEST THAT EVER WAS! SPUNTO!

SHA CABROOL, IT IS WITH ALL DUE RESPECT THAT I TELL YOU YOU ARE MAKING A MISTAKE.

"ALL DUE RESPECT"? WHAT RESPECT IS NOT DUE ME? YOU TRAITOR?

SHOW THE TRAITOR TO HIS ROOM, AND KEEP AN EYE ON HIM. DON'T TRY TO LEAVE THE HOUSE, JABBA; THE GUARDS WILL TURN YOU INTO A RUG.

A HIDEOUS, FLABBY RUG.

I REPEAT, YOU'RE MAKING A MISTAKE.

THAT'S WHAT EVERY TRAITOR I'VE EVER BURIED HAS TOLD ME...DO THE SMART THING, JABBA. I'LL SEE YOU IN THE MORNING.

LET ME PASS, LONKA.

MY ORDERS ARE TO LET NO ONE IN OR OUT.

DO YOU WANT ME TO TELL MY FATHER YOU TOOK THE MISSING STUMPWEED?

I OUGHT TO STRANGLE YOU, BRAT.

MAY I HAVE A WORD WITH YOU?

OF COURSE, BOY.

I DON'T HAVE TO TELL YOU THAT MY FATHER IS LOSING HIS SANITY.

IT LOOKS THAT WAY TO ME.

IT WOULD BE BEST FOR ALL CONCERNED IF HE WERE TO JUST DIE.

HUH. WHY DON'T YOU GIVE HIM A NUDGE IN THAT DIRECTION?

NONE OF US HAVE THE NERVE. EVEN THE GUARDS... HE HAS TOO MUCH AUTHORITY OVER US. BUT WE ALL WANT TO.

HUH.

BUT YOU COULD DO IT.

HUH.

I'LL GET YOU INTO HIS BEDROOM, AND YOU CAN KILL HIM IN HIS SLEEP.

HUH.

IT'S THE ONLY WAY YOU'LL GET OUT OF HERE. EVEN IF YOU DID KILL YU CHUSKER, DAD WOULD FIND A REASON TO ELIMINATE YOU. HE'S KILLED EVERY ONE OF HIS FRIENDS.

YOU'VE PERSUADED ME, BOY. WHAT KIND OF TOOL WILL I HAVE?

THERE ARE NO WEAPONS IN THE HOUSE; DAD WON'T EVEN ALLOW KNIVES SINCE HE'S GOTTEN SO SUSPICIOUS OF EVERYONE. YOU'LL HAVE TO THROTTLE HIM.

I'LL DO IT.

WROCK! WUK WASSSK!

HE'S DEAD.

WHEW! WHAT A JOB THAT WAS.

IT'S FOR THE BEST. HE WASN'T HIMSELF ANYMORE.

AND THAT MAKES ME THE BOSS AROUND HERE.

YES, SIR.

JABBA.

I *KNEW* THIS WOULD HAPPEN WHEN RUSK TOOK OVER DAD'S JOB!

STUPID KID.

OH, I KNOW. HE'S ALWAYS WANTED POWER BUT THERE'S NO WAY HE CAN HANDLE IT.

I WANTED TO ASK YOU... DID YOU EVER MEET MY MOTHER?

UH...YES... YES I DID. MANY TIMES.

SHE WAS REALLY THE FORCE BEHIND MY FATHER -- EXCEPT FOR THE TRULY AWFUL STUFF HE DID.

YES... ADMIRABLE BEING.

I WANT TO RESTORE THE FAMILY HONOR BY RETURNING TO HER WAY OF DOING THINGS. TO DO THIS I MUST BE IN CHARGE.

HM.

FOR ME TO BE IN CHARGE RUSK MUST DIE.

HMN.

I CAN'T DO IT. YOU MUST HELP ME.

HMNT. GLADLY.

FOLLOW ME.

WE'LL TELL HIM YOU'VE CHANGED YOUR MIND AND THAT YOU'RE WILLING TO KILL YU CHUSKER NOW.

THEN I'LL DISTRACT HIM AND YOU BASH HIS BRAINS IN.

SIMPLE, DIRECT... GOOD PLAN. WHAT ABOUT THE GUARDS?

RUSK HAS SENT THEM OUT TO GET HIM SOME FEMALES. HE'S SUCH A WHOG.

BIZAP.

BIZAP, BIZAP...

GOOD NEWS, RUSK; JABBA'S RECONSIDERED.

WHAT?

IT'S TRUE. I CONCEDE THAT YOU WERE RIGHT TO ASK FOR A TOKEN OF MY ALLEGIANCE.

THIS IS A TRICK!

THE END

GRAPHIC NOVELS

ALIENS
- ☐ 0 7522 0878 0   Aliens v Preator – Deadliest of the Species 1   £9.99 pb
- ☐ 0 7522 0695 8   Aliens v Preator – Deadliest of the Species 2   £9.99 pb

RANMA
- ☐ 0 7522 0851 9   Ranma Book 1   £5.99 pb
- ☐ 0 7522 0861 6   Ranma Book 2   £5.99 pb

SPIDER-MAN
- ☐ 0 7522 0107 7   Masques   £8.99 pb
- ☐ 0 7522 0112 3   Perceptions   £8.99 pb
- ☐ 0 7522 0876 4   The Return of the Sinister 6   £9.99 pb
- ☐ 0 7522 0808 X   Revenge of the Sinister 6   £7.99 pb

STAR WARS
- ☐ 0 7522 0893 4   Classic – A New Hope   £8.99 pb
- ☐ 0 7522 0987 6   Dark Empire   £9.99 pb
- ☐ 0 7522 0822 5   Dark Empire 2   £9.99 pb
- ☐ 0 7522 0793 8   Dark Empire/Epilogue   £6.99 pb
- ☐ 0 7522 0616 8   Dark Lords of Sith 1   £8.99 pb
- ☐ 0 7522 0804 7   Droids   £8.99 pb
- ☐ 0 7522 0606 0   Empire Strikes Back   £7.99 pb
- ☐ 0 7522 0704 0   Jabba the Hutt   £8.99 pb
- ☐ 0 7522 0611 7   Return of the Jedi   £7.99 pb
- ☐ 0 7522 0798 9   River of Chaos   £8.99 pb
- ☐ 0 7522 0913 2   Star Wars Classic   £7.99 pb
- ☐ 0 7522 0747 4   Star Wars Classic 2   £9.99 pb
- ☐ 0 7522 0752 0   Star Wars Classic 3   £9.99 pb
- ☐ 0 7522 0817 9   Tales of the Jedi and Freedom Nadd Uprising   £10.99 pb

STAR TREK – DEEP SPACE NINE
- ☐ 0 7522 0928 0   Emancipation 1   £7.99 pb
- ☐ 0 7522 0933 7   Emancipation and Beyond   £7.99 pb
- ☐ 0 7522 0898 5   Hearts and Minds   £7.99 pb
- ☐ 0 7522 0888 8   Requiem   £7.99 pb

STREETFIGHTER
- ☐ 0 7522 0813 6   Street Fighter II – book 1   £6.99 pb
- ☐ 0 7522 0818 7   Street Fighter II – book 2   £6.99 pb

VARIOUS
- ☐ 0 7522 0897 7   Daredevil – man without fear   £9.99 pb
- ☐ 0 7522 0962 0   Necroscope   £7.99 pb
- ☐ 0 7522 0645 1   Marvels   £10.99 pb
- ☐ 0 7522 0881 0   Mask (film tie-in)   £6.99 pb
- ☐ 0 7522 0977 9   RoboCop: Prime Suspect   £7.99 pb
- ☐ 0 7522 0856 X   Shadow (film tie-in)   £6.99 pb
- ☐ 0 7522 0762 8   Species Movie (tie-in)   £8.99 pb

X MEN
- ☐ 0 7522 0892 6   Adventures   £9.99 pb
- ☐ 1 85283 390 4   Brood Trouble In The Big Easy   £5.25 pb
- ☐ 1 85283 394 7   Essential Guide   £9.99 pb
- ☐ 0 7522 0756 3   Gambit   £7.99 pb
- ☐ 0 7522 0691 5   Ghostrider/Wolverine/Punisher/Hearts of Darkness/Dark Design   £7.99 pb
- ☐ 0 7522 0871 3   God Loves, Man Kills   £5.99 pb
- ☐ 0 7522 0103 4   Rogue   £8.99 pb
- ☐ 0 7522 0803 9   Sabretooth   £6.99 pb
- ☐ 1 85283 395 5   Wolverine   £6.99 pb
- ☐ 0 7522 0108 5   Wolverine – Triumph and Tragedy   £9.99 pb
- ☐ 0 7522 0151 4   Uncanny X-Men: Acts of Vengeance   £8.99 pb
- ☐ 0 7522 0161 1   Uncanny X-Men: Wolverine/Psylocke 1   £8.99 pb

All these books are available at your local bookshop or can be ordered direct from the publisher. Just tick the titles you want and fill in the form below.

Prices and availability subject to change without notice.

Boxtree Cash Sales, P.O. Box 11, Falmouth, Cornwall TR10 9EN

Please send a cheque or postal order for the value of the book and add the following for postage and packing:

U.K. including B.F.P.O. – £1.00 for one book plus 50p for the second book, and 30p for each additional book ordered up to a £3.00 maximum.

Overseas including Eire – £2.00 for the first book plus £1.00 for the second book, and 50p for each additional book ordered.

OR please debit this amount from my Access/Visa Card (delete as appropriate).

Card Number ☐☐☐☐ ☐☐☐☐ ☐☐☐☐ ☐☐☐☐

Amount £ ....

Expiry Date ....

Signed ....

Name ....

Address ....